Pang the Penguin™
presents
The First Splish Splash

Book One: Water Safety and Pool Adventure Series

by Lotta D. Todd
Illustrations by Mike Motz

Preface

An important message from our water safety friend,
Pang the Penguin:

1. Remember: safety first.

2. Have fun, but stay safe in and around water.

3. Follow the pool rules.

4. The most important rule is "no swimming alone!"

In loving memory of our little angel, Yaya,
who inspires me,
stays on my mind,
and will always live in my heart.

This book is dedicated
to my mom and dad, Doris and Leonard,
brother Travis, and
three daughters Chevon, Chanel, and Chamone.

ISBN: 978-1-7371139-1-1 (hardcover),
ISBN: 978-1-7371139-0-4 (paperback)
ISBN: 978-1-7371139-2-8 (ebook)

Langston kicks his feet and rotates his arms faster
than ever as he stretches his fingertips toward the pool wall.

"Langston wins!" the crowd shouts as he pops up from the water.

Judges crown him the "Best Swimmer" while he holds his trophy for the whole world to see. But it is all a dream.

Langston shares his vivid dream with his parents and water safety friend, Pang the Penguin.
"That's a great dream, son!" his dad says. "Learn how to swim, and you can make your dream come true."

"Cool things can happen when you're a super swimmer like me," Pang brags.
"Like what?" Langston asks.

"You will have a lot of fun. Plus, you will build confidence and your muscles, too," Pang says.

Langston's eyes widen as he turns to his parents.
"Can we please go to the pool?" Langston asks.
"That's a great idea!" his parents reply. "Let's go on Saturday!"

It's Saturday, Langston's big day!
He grabs a small backpack from his closet
and an oversized towel from the bathroom.
Hmm...is that it? he wonders.

Langston's mom surprises him with a large shopping bag.
His eyes widen and light up like a Christmas tree.

First, he pulls out a brand-new pair of swim trunks and matching goggles. "Aaaah. . . swim trunks and goggles!"

"Yes, you have to wear your swim trunks at the pool," Pang says, "and the goggles will help protect your eyes and help you see clearly once your face is in the water."

Second, Langston pulls out a brand-new swim cap.
"What's this hat for?" Langston asks.
"It will help protect your hair, keep it out of your eyes,
and make you a faster swimmer too," Pang explains.

Next, Langston pulls out a small tube. "What's this?"
"That is sunscreen – your body armor," Pang replies.
"It protects your skin from sunburn. The sun's rays are mighty hot!"

Then, Langston sees a bright orange swim vest in the bag.
"I know what this is!" Langston says.
"It will help me float until I learn how to swim."

Finally, it's POOL TOYS!
"Thanks, Mom! You're the best!" Langston says
as she kisses him on the cheek.

On their way to the pool, Langston sings,
"It's time to go and have some fun,
in the pool, in the pool.

It's time to go and have some fun.
Fun! Fun! Fun!"

They arrive at the pool.
It's time to splish-splash the day away.
But the pool gate is locked. "Oh no!" Langston says

SWIMMING POOL RULES
No rough play
No swimming alone
No diving in shallow end
Keep gate closed and locked
No running
No glass allowed
No peeing or pooping in pool
Swimsuits required

"It stays locked to stop children from entering the pool area alone.
That keeps everyone safe," Pang explains.
Langston's mom explains that the pool is a lot of fun,
but it can be dangerous if you are not careful.
"Never enter the pool area alone, even if the entrance gate is
unlocked or open," she says as she unlocks the gate.

As they enter the pool area, Langston sees children swimming, floating, and splashing in the pool.

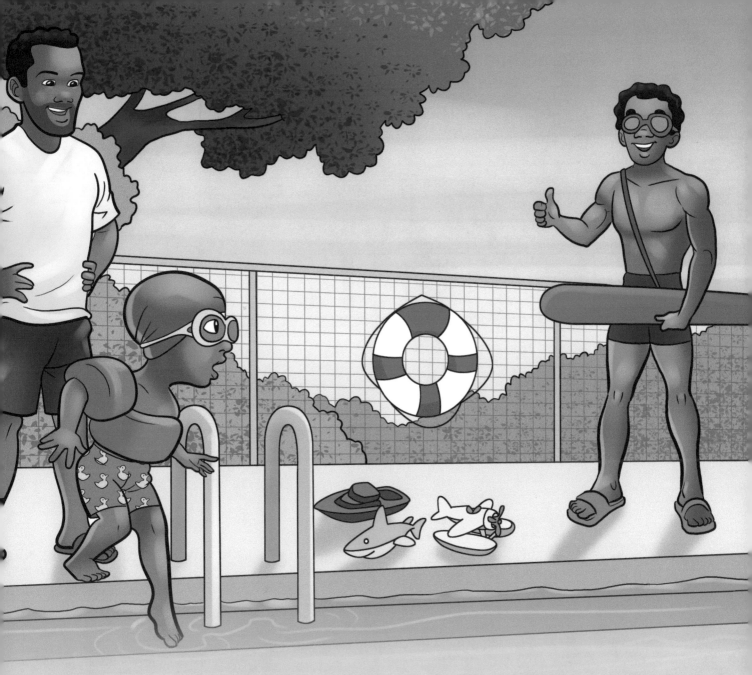

"Are you ready to get in?" his dad asks.
Langston hesitates as he looks at the lifeguard for reassurance.
Then, Langston bravely dips his toes into the shallow water.
"Brrrr! That's cold!" Langston shouts as he quickly steps back.

Langston takes a deep breath and jumps feet first into the pool, making his first splish splash!

She guides him to the stairs where he sits
and plays with his pool toys.
The water is feeling warmer and warmer.

Then, they kick their legs up and down as hard as they can while challenging the splashes to reach the sky.

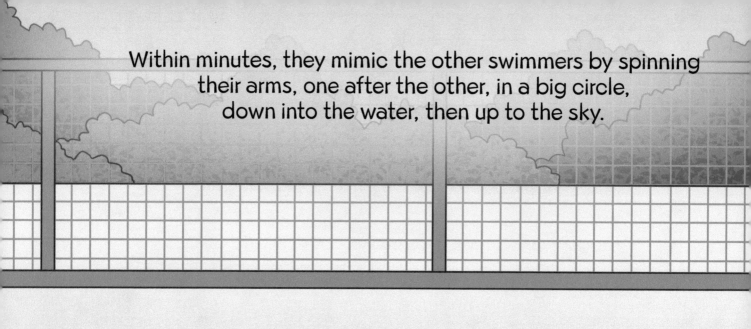

Within minutes, they mimic the other swimmers by spinning their arms, one after the other, in a big circle, down into the water, then up to the sky.

"Watch out world. Here I come!
I'm going to be the best of the best.
I'm going to be number one!"

WHAT DID YOU LEARN FROM TODAY'S WATER SAFETY AND POOL ADVENTURE?

• Never go swimming alone. Always swim with an adult, buddy, and lifeguard.

• Locked pool gates keep everyone safe.

• Always jump feet first into the shallow end of the pool.

• Beginners stay in the shallow end, close to the stairs where it is safe.

• Wear sunscreen to protect your skin from sunburn.

• Wear your swimsuit or swim trunks while swimming at the pool.

• Wear goggles to protect your eyes and to help you see underwater clearly.

• Wear a swim cap to help you swim faster, protect your hair, and keep it out of your eyes.

GLOSSARY

Confidence: Feeling good and trusting one's own powers and ability to succeed.

Goggles: Eyeglasses that fit snuggly over the eyes to protect them.

Lifeguard: A professional rescuer who makes sure everyone stays healthy and safe in and around water.

Safety: To be safe and protected from harm.

Sunburn: Skin damage caused by too much exposure to the sun's ultraviolet (UV) rays.

Sunscreen: Sun Protection Factor (SPF) body cream or spray that absorbs the ultraviolet (UV) rays to prevent skin damage. SPF 30 or higher is recommended.

Swim cap: Skin tight cap that is worn on the head by recreational and competitive swimmers.

Swim vest: Flotation device that keeps the body afloat. Not a substitute for supervision.

Swimsuit: Clothing worn during water sports, swimming, and sunbathing activities.

Did you know...

• Drowning is the leading cause of unintentional deaths for children ages 1 – 9 years old.

• Approximately 64% African-American, 45% Hispanic/Latino, and 40% Caucasian children have few or no swimming skills.

• Drownings are preventable.

• No one is drown-proof, and drowning does not discriminate.

• Approximately ten drownings occur per day.

Source: stopdrowningnow.org

Join Pang the Penguin and friends for more fantastic pool adventures.

Sponsored by

Splash Rite Swim School LLC

Splash Rite. Swim Right. Save a Life.

Acknowledgements

First, thank you to my granddaughter, Eden, who created our friend, Pang the Penguin, long before Pang became a famous water safety guru.

Thank you to my three amazing daughters, Chevon, Chanel, and Chamone, who through their support, own individual life experiences, and wisdom provided feedback that was instrumental in the creation of *The First Splish Splash.*

Thank you to my editor, Starr, who is not only my editor, but also my mentor whom I greatly appreciate.

Thank you to my friend, Renard, who provided meaningful guidance, support, and answers throughout the creation of *The First Splish Splash.*

Finally, last but not least, I thank my students who bless me with memorable experiences in the pool that will provide entertaining material for Pang the Penguin's water safety and pool adventure series for years to come.

About the Author

Lotta D. Todd has 20 years of experience in the aquatic industry. She is certified as an Aquatic Facility Operator (AFO). Todd is skilled as a Lifeguard, Swim Coach, and Instructor who has taught 3,000 students. She is a member of the National Drowning Prevention Alliance and Drowning Prevention Coalition in Arizona. Todd volunteers for Phoenix Children's Hospital and partners with Pool Safely, Yaya's Halo, and several local retailers to promote water safety awareness and swim lessons for everyone.

CPSIA information can be obtained
at www.ICGtesting.com
Printed in the USA
BVHW022152200821
614851BV00008B/702